Would you consider partnering with Lynn and Foster Friess and Molly and George Greene in the Million Dollar Challenge Grant to provide safe water around the world?

...or.

...tional

...their contributions to this book.

...m), 2012.

...otherwise noted.

...issions International book a reality.

*This book was purposely produced in hard copy in hopes you would keep
it on your coffee table as a conversation piece to inspire your visiting
friends and neighbors. Its costs were incurred by an anonymous don*

*Please contact George or Molly Greene to learn how to acquire add
copies of this book to send to your family and friends.*

Water for a Thirsty World

Dear Friends,

It is our prayer that this book will open your eyes to the global water crisis that so many of our brothers and sisters in developing countries experience every day. Nearly 884 million people lack the most basic of human needs: safe water. Another 2.6 billion people have no decent sanitation facilities. And, even worse, a child dies every 20 seconds from a disease related to unsafe water and poor sanitation.

These statistics are not acceptable. What if this were your child? Would you not be doing everything you could to change the situation? You can. **Water Missions International** has the solution. We have the technology to treat any type of contaminated water and we have the ability to provide basic sanitation. What we lack are the financial resources to make a more significant impact in developing countries. We need your help!

Water Missions International is a nonprofit Christian Engineering Ministry providing sustainable safe water solutions to people in developing countries and disaster areas. Since its inception in 2001, **Water Missions International** has provided an opportunity for more than two million people in 49 countries to receive safe water and the Living Water message.

Our prayer is that you will join our efforts as we seek to respond to our Lord's call "to love our neighbors as ourselves" by providing safe water!

Blessings,

George + Molly

George and Molly Greene
Founders, Water Missions International
Charleston, South Carolina, USA

Thank you for partnering with us to provide the most basic of human needs – safe water!

The Global Water Crisis

884 million people lack access to safe water.

That's one out of every eight people.

WHO (2010)

Water and Health

More than **5,000** children die every day worldwide from diseases caused by unsafe water and poor sanitation.

Together, lack of safe water and sanitation are the world's largest causes of illness.

UNICEF, Progress for Children (2006)
U.N. Report (2005)

Water and Poverty

Of the **884 million** people without safe water, two-thirds
live on less than $2 per day.

Unsafe water is both a cause and effect of poverty.

Water and Sanitation

More than **2.6 billion** people do not have access to latrines or any sort of basic sanitary facilities.

That's four out of every ten people.

UNWater (2010)

Water, Women and Girls

African women often spend as much as **8 hours per day** collecting water. Girls are typically given the task of collecting water, carrying 15 to 20 liters (weighing 33 to 45 pounds).

In many developing countries, girls often choose not to attend schools that do not have latrines out of concern for their privacy and modesty.

U.N. Task Force on Gender and Water (2004)

Water and Natural Disasters

Water is often the most critical need after natural disasters such as earthquakes, hurricanes or floods.

Water Missions International is a nonprofit Christian Engineering Ministry providing sustainable safe water solutions to people in developing countries and disaster areas.

"The water project is a blessing because there were families drinking water straight from the river which is a very contaminated source, and now they are drinking clean water. They are getting less sick. But where I see the most blessing is at school.... my kids are drinking very good water when before we had to buy expensive water to give them in their water bottles. We always praise the good LORD for Water Missions Belize."

Cesar Gutierrez, board member of the safe water committee of Billy White village, Belize

Water Missions International designs sustainable safe water solutions that meet the specific needs of each community we serve. The Living Water™ Treatment System (LWTS™) is commonly used.

"Because of clean water, for the first time ever, no one is sick in my entire family!"

Pastor Jose Encino Lopez, Mexico

The LWTS™ works like a mini water treatment plant and can purify more than **10,000 gallons** of water per day. That's enough for 3,000–5,000 people.

"I am very grateful to God for the gift that they gave us through Water Missions International. It has been a blessing to us. Since we got the system our lives have changed, we now get clean and safe water. My children are no longer going to have stomachaches and diarrhea and they will not miss school as a result. I believe they will perform better since they can now concentrate on their studies."

Lorna Chepkesio, Cheminy, Kenya

TO THE GLORY OF GOD
THIS LIVING WATER TREATMENT
SYSTEM WAS DONATED BY WATER
MISSIONS INTERNATIONAL TO
MIMA SCHOOL AND COMMUNITY.
IT WAS OFFICIALLY COMMISSIONED
BY MR. GEORGE GREEN IV CEO
WATER MISSIONS INTERNATIONAL
ON 25TH SEP. 2008.

Water Missions
International

The LWTS™ can be assembled on site in **15 minutes.**
This is vital in disaster response.

"My family has changed a lot thanks to this system, everyone in my family are in good health, we do not get sick by consuming contaminated water anymore, this equipment allows me to prepare lemonade with the delicious lemon from the area, we are very grateful. The operational cost is very affordable because families in our community are very poor, and we save money because we do not buy wood or gas."

Velasquez Rengifo Family, Ex Petroleros, Peru

And if anyone gives even a cup of cold water to one of these little ones because he is my disciple, I tell you the truth, he will certainly not lose his reward.

Matthew 10:42 (NIV)

"Almost everyone in the church is using the water. The kids are now helping themselves to water when they are thirsty, they never did this before. Now they can walk up to the bucket, turn the tap, and pour their own clean water to drink and they all feel better."

Jonathan Montejo Diaz, 6 years old, Suclumpa, Chiapas, Mexico

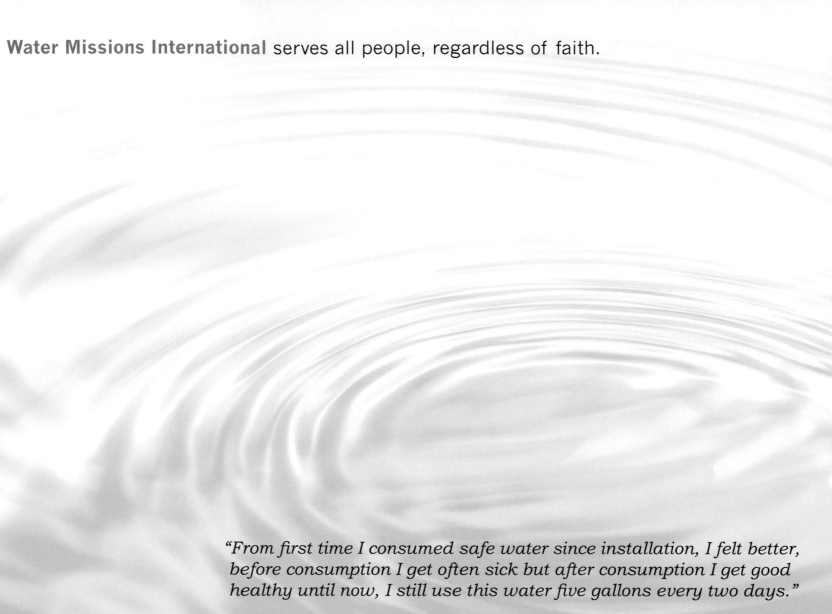

Water Missions International serves all people, regardless of faith.

"From first time I consumed safe water since installation, I felt better, before consumption I get often sick but after consumption I get good healthy until now, I still use this water five gallons every two days."

Mr. Cornelius, Alak Village, Kupang, East Nusa Tenggara, Indonesia

Water Missions International serves all people, regardless of age or gender.

"On behalf the Prince of Peace Church, we are very grateful with Water Missions for this benefit that we have received from yours. We know that through this project we are receiving physical health for our children and adult people thanks for your effort you are doing a great job."

Obeniel León, Pastor Prince of Peace Church, Cuyamel, Trujillo, Colón, Honduras

Water Missions International serves all people, regardless of race.

"This water is very helpful not only for the school and surrounding community but also others from elsewhere. School enrollment has risen from 1,400 pupils to about 1,800 now."

Nicodemus Msukwa, Chitipa, Malawi

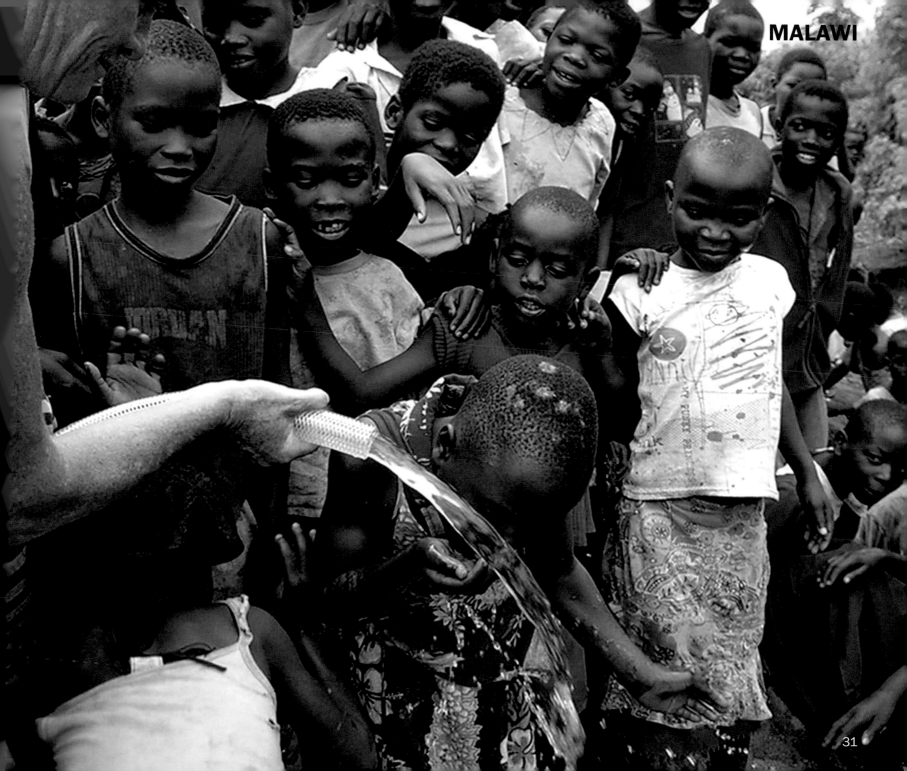

Water Missions International serves all people, regardless of ability to pay.

"On behalf of the Water Commission from Vista Hermosa Community we are grateful with Water Missions International for the donation of this safe water system we know the benefit when we are drinking safe water for our children and adult people physical health, thanks again for your support. We are willing to help everyone have access to this project and we will work to give safe water everyone. Thanks and God Bless You."

Henry Dias, Safe Water Committee President, Trujillo, Colon, Honduras

Water Missions International has provided access to safe water for more than **two million** people in 49 countries around the world.

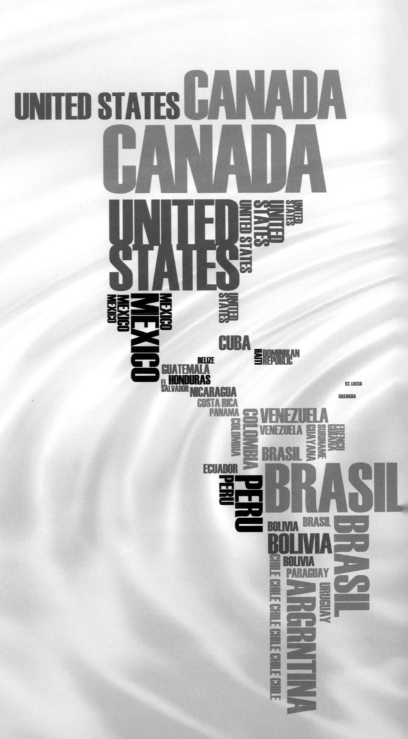

■ **Country programs with full-time staff**

■ **Countries served to date**

Water Missions International utilizes solar power so that people living in even the most remote places around the world can receive safe water.

"This water has helped many people in the community, especially the children who had to travel long distances to get water from the well through fast moving and reckless driving. The system has also helped old and the needy people who could not buy water that cost so much. People are happy because they no longer boil water for drinking which saves both money and time."

Sarah Wanyana, Operator, Nakinyuguzi, Uganda

Water Missions International engineers design sustainable safe water solutions and engage community members to install, operate and maintain these solutions.

"I participated fully during the construction and installation of the water system right from the start during formulation of the safe water committee, trenching for pipes, construction of the enclosure, and health and hygiene training... water is available all the time and very close to home so that I do not have to walk a long distance to collect it as was before."

Fred, Nakinyuguzi, Uganda

Water Missions International teaches community members about healthy water, sanitation and hygiene behavior.

"After we had the water machine installed in my well, we could see the difference in the quality of the water with what we had before, and how clean the water was after this machine treated it. We did not understand why Water Missions was helping us and always came to check our water, asking us if we liked it, until they said this was the command God gave them to help their brothers and sisters who are suffering. Now we see our children drinking more water and they are not sick like before."

Andre Louis, Haiti

Water Missions International builds latrines, bringing sanitation and dignity to families and individuals in developing countries.

"The members of the local Safe Water and Sanitation Commission thank each of you for having helped this project. We greatly appreciate your valuable donation; this is a great blessing to our neighborhood."

Enique Fuentes, Sonaguera, Colon, Honduras

Water Missions International provides an opportunity to hear the Living Water message of Jesus.

Jesus answered, "Whoever drinks the water I give him will never thirst. Indeed, the water I give him will become a wellspring of water, welling up to eternal life."

John 4:14 (NIV)

Volunteers are a vital part of **Water Missions International.**
Without their help, the mission could not be achieved.

"Since retiring, Water Missions International has provided a way for me to give back some of what God has so generously given me. I thoroughly enjoy working with a Christian organization and with the many men and women here."

Dick Johnson, Charleston, South Carolina

"This is a picture of five men that give their time, talent and love to supply Living Water to those around the world that need it. You can see by our smiles that we enjoy what we do and who we do it for. This ministry gives the hearts of those who work in it a lot of good, but most of all it helps the hearts of those that receive this Living Water."

Gene Lesesne, Charleston, South Carolina

There are still millions of people who lack access to safe water. **Water Missions International** will not stop working until the global water crisis has ended.

"The living conditions of the residents of Desfourneaux is very bad. Most of the population is very poor and they have very little money to survive. The water situation is even worse, the Artibonite river is very contaminated with bacteria including cholera. The merchants throw all the market trash into the river. Also the meat sellers kill the animals by the river and throw all the non-eatable parts into the river. Many people get sick very often and many die because of diarrhea and even cholera."

Pastor Dupheline Dieulifaite, Desfourneaux Village, Artibonite Department, Haiti

People are waiting, and many containers still need to be filled with safe water. Water Missions International invites you to help provide safe and Living Water for those who thirst!

"The water is safe for drinking, cooking, washing and bathing. Before the installation of the water system, we used to fetch water from a borehole 1.5 km away, but the water was not safe. Whenever we pumped, the water would come out with worms, and a brownish color. Cases of typhoid among students were common in the school. I was once admitted in Kumi Hospital because of typhoid."

Solomon Imalingat (Senior Three), Bishop Ilukor Secondary School, Uganda

Water Missions International gives lasting hope to people in need. Thank you for joining us in the fight against the global water crisis.

UGANDA

52

"If you want to go fast, go alone.
If you want to go far, go together."

-African Proverb

Together, we can go far in bringing safe water to people in need.

Water Missions
International †

P.O. Box 31258 | Charleston, SC 29417 USA
(p) 843.769.7395 | (toll free) 866.280.7107 | (f) 843.763.6082
www.watermissions.org

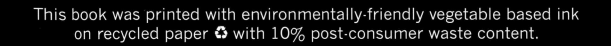